...o keep thoughts and feelings

belongs to

_____

Begun | | | |
DATE

Here's how some view this mysterious new book toy to help you write your thoughts:

"...AN INSTRUCTIONAL WORK FOR BOTH CHILDREN AND ADULTS, aimed at helping them learn to keep their own diaries and journals...after answering the several dozen questions, a diary is born, and with it, one presumes, a lifelong habit."

—*Esquire*

"...COULD BE THE PERFECT MOTIVATOR FOR THE CHILD WHO NEEDS A LITTLE PUSH TO GET STARTED ON KEEPING A JOURNAL...An appealing, tiny paperback, "A BOOK OF QUESTIONS" is a nice size to tuck into pockets or overnight bags and take out in spare moments."

—*Gifted Children Newsletter*

"Much has been written about how executives can learn to deal with stress. But executives who are too busy to read about stress can write about it instead in "A BOOK OF QUESTIONS"...ZIMMERMAN IS TRYING TO GET INDIVIDUALS TO THINK ABOUT THEMSELVES AND THEIR WORLDS FOR A FEW MINUTES DAILY...as a way of putting their lives in perspective and reducing anxieties."

—*Gannett Westchester Newspapers*

A BOOK OF QUESTIONS

to keep thoughts and feelings

By William Zimmerman

A way to break away and touch base with yourself

Your answers create your own
Journal of Thoughts

GUARIONEX PRESS LTD.
Publisher
New York

For Carlota, who has so many questions
May you find the answers,
and never take "no" for an answer.

A BOOK OF QUESTIONS
To keep thoughts and feelings

Copyright 1984
by William Zimmerman
3rd ptng, 1986. 4th ptng, 1987. 5th ptng, 1988.
6th ptng, 1989. 7th ptng, 1990. 8th ptng, 1991.

For information write to:
William Zimmerman,Guarionex Press Ltd.
201 West 77 Street, New York, NY 10024
Or call 212-724-5259

The author welcomes your comments on the questions offered in this book as well as ideas for questions you would like to see added in future editions.

Library of Congress
Catalog Card Number: 82 083403

Special thanks to Arthur Hamparian

Book design by Eileen Berasi

FOREWORD

This little book will be unlike any other you have read because it will be written by you. It will hold the thoughts and feelings that belong only to you.

So many of us say we want to keep a journal, but when we decide to try, we're not quite sure what to write in it.

This book will enable you to begin, because it provides a simple way for you to think about your life: it questions you and encourages you to respond with written thoughts.

And such writing will help you decipher yourself.

The questions in this book are there to help you talk to and know yourself better through your written responses to them. They are questions I have asked myself throughout my life. I believe they will have meaning for you, too.

They are here to help you take your pulse, to hear your special voice.

The book was made small, to be carried on your person like some bible that contains the clearest moments of your life when you took the time to write to yourself.

Its questions are meant to free you, to amuse you, to puzzle you, to help you break away from the hard work you do.

Choose the ones you want to answer in any order; feel free to change them to meet your own needs—they are merely a guide. Simply write whatever thoughts come to mind in the space provided under the question, and add to them with time. There also is a place to write the date for the thought.

Don't worry if you don't have answers to a particular question. Come back to it when you feel ready. There are blank pages in the back to add your own questions. And, when you run out of space, begin another journal.

Write in this book only when you want to. You may even want to draw your answers or write your thoughts in your own secret language.

This little book is yours to define yourself; but it can be shared with those whom you want to know more about you.

Enjoy my book of questions. Through use it becomes your Journal of Thoughts and Feelings. Remember, once you complete it, there will be no other book like it in the world. It is created by you. Start this book when you are ready to listen to yourself.

WEZ

P.S. To encourage you in your search for answers, a secret message has been placed in the Morse code lines on which you write your responses, on the pages inside. It is there for you to decipher—should you wish—with help from the printed code key.

Listen to your voice. It will give you answers.

MEANINGS:

1. Child 2. Universe 3. Knowledge 4. Four Ages of Man (Infancy, Youth, Middle and Old Age) 5. Finding 6. Abundance 7. Good Prospects 8. Everlasting Life 9. Light

The broken lines in this book on which you write your thoughts and feelings hold a secret message for you written in Morse code should you choose to decipher it. You can write your thoughts between or on top of the lines. You can even write your thoughts in the code which follows:

```
A . __      B __ . . .     C __ . __ .     D __ . .
E .      F . . __ .     G __ __ .     H . . . .     I . .
J . __ __ __     K __ . __     L . __ . .
M __ __     N __ .     O __ __ __
P . __ __ .     Q __ __ . __     R . __ .
S . . .     T __     U . . __     V . . . __
W . __ __     X __ . . __     Y __ . __ __
Z __ __ . .     . __ . __ . __
? . . __ __ . .     ! __ . __ . __ __
```

Enjoy your thoughts.

What have been the happiest times of
your life?

*(You can write your thoughts between or on
top of the following broken lines.)*

| **Thoughts:** | DATE | | | |

.__   ...   ._   _   _.. ___

_.__   ___   .._   _   ...   ..

_.   _._   .._.   .   .   ._..

_..   .   .___   ..   .   .__   .

..   ___..   _..   ___   _.

___   _   __...   .   ._   .._.

._.   .   ..   _..   _

——— ·—— ·—· ·· — ·

—·· ——— ·—— —· —·——

——— ··— ·—· ··· ·——·

· —·—· ·· ·— ·—·· — ····

——— ··— ——· ···· — ···

·— —· —·· ··—· · · ·—··

·· —· ——· ··· ·—·—·—

·—— ···· ·— — —·· ———

—·—— ——— ··— — ···· ··

My journal of thoughts and feelings

What special thing happened to you today?

Thoughts: DATE | | |

.-- .... .- — -. ---

-.-- --- ..- .-- ...- ..

-. -.- ..- -. — .-

-... . .-— .. -. .

..-—- —.. --- — -.

--- — -.. . .- — ..-.

.-. .- .. — .. ..

My journal of thoughts and feelings

What's funny about yourself that
makes you smile when you think of it?

`.-- ... .-- - - -.. ---`

`-.-- --- ... . ..`

`-. .- ..-. . . -..`

`-.. . .-- - .`

`..-.. -.. --- -.`

`--- - -.. . .- ..-.`

`.-. .- -`

`--- .-- .-. ..`

My journal of thoughts and feelings

If you had three magic wishes that could come true, what would they be? (You don't have to write them down all at once.)

Thoughts:

.-- ... .- — — -.. ---

—.-- --- .. — — ... ..

—. —.- .-.- . . —..

—... . .- .. . ...- .

..——.. —.. --- —.

--- — —.. . .- —..

.- .- .. —.. —

--- .-- .-. ..

My journal of thoughts and feelings

Thoughts:

.—— ... .— — —.. ———

—.— ——— ..— — ... ..

—. —.— .—.— . .—..

—.. . .—.. ... .

..——.. —.. ——— —.

——— — —... . .— ..—.

.—. — .. —.— —

——— .—. .—. ..

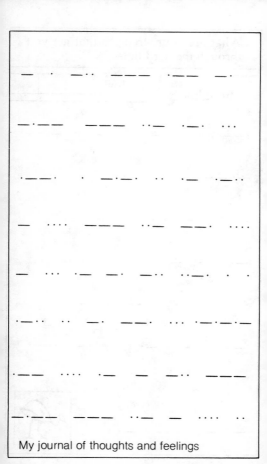

My journal of thoughts and feelings

What's your favorite story?

Thoughts: DATE [ ][ ][ ]

.-- .... .- -- - -.. ---

-.-- --- ..- - - .... ..

-. -.- .-. . . .-..

-... . .-- .. . .

..--. -.. --- --.

--- - -.. . .- ..-.

.-. .- .- -.. -

--- .-- .-. ..

My journal of thoughts and feelings

If there were to be no tomorrow, what
would you do today?

Thoughts:

`.__ ... ._ _ _.. ___`

`_.__ ___ .._ _ ... ..`

`_. _._ .._. . . ._..`

`_.. . ._. . . ... .`

`.._.._ _.. ___ _.`

`___ _ _.. . ._ .._.`

`._. ._. .. _. _.`

`___ ._. ._ ..`

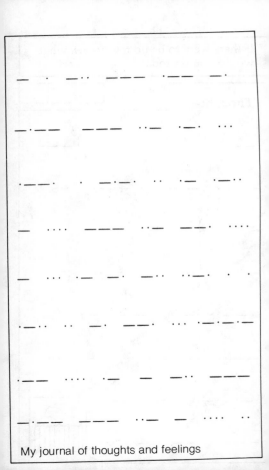

My journal of thoughts and feelings

What is the most important piece of information you've picked up in life so
far?

Thoughts: DATE [ ][ ][ ]

.___ ... ._ _ _.. ___

_._ ___ .._ _ ... ..

_. _._ ..._ . . ._.

_.. . ._.. .. . .

.._.._ _.. ___ _.

___ _ _.. . ._ ._.

._ ._ . .. _. _

My journal of thoughts and feelings

If you could create something very beautiful for the world, what would it be?

Thoughts: DATE [ ][ ][ ]

.— ... .— — —.. ———

—.—— ——— ..— — .... ..

—. —.— ..—. . . .—.

—... .—.— . . ... .

..——.. —.. ——— —.

——— — —... . .— ..—.

.—. .— .. — —

——— .—. .—. ..

My journal of thoughts and feelings

What makes you most happy?

.-- ... .- - - -.. .--

-.-- - --- .-- - .... ..

-. .-. .-. . . ... .-.

-... . .-.. .. . . ..-

..-.. -.. --- -.

--- - -.. . .- ..-.

.-. .- .. ..

--- .-. .. -.

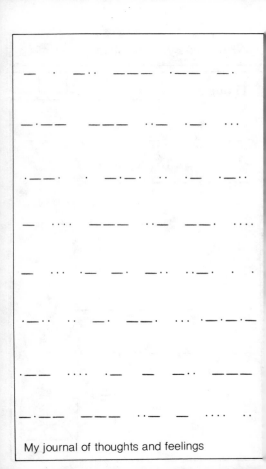

My journal of thoughts and feelings

What new things would you like to do?

Thoughts:

DATE

.-- .... .- - _ -.. ---

-.- --- ... - _ -.. ..

-. --. ..-. . . .-..

-... . .-.. .. . .

..-.. -.. --. -.. . _ -.

--- - -... . . ..-.

.-. .- .. -.. - _

--- .-- -. .. ..

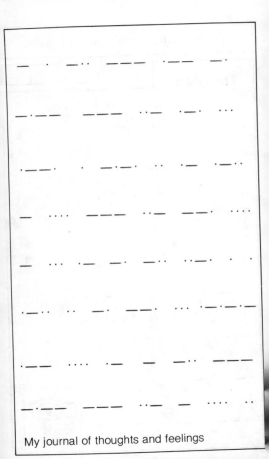

My journal of thoughts and feelings

What bad memory or dream keeps playing over and over in your head like a broken melody?

Thoughts:

DATE ☐ ☐ ☐

```
.-- ...  .-   —   —..   ---

-.--   ---   ..-   —   ....   ..

-.   -.-   ...   .   .-.

-...   .   .-..   ..   .   ...   .

..-..   -..   ---   —   -.

---   —   -...   .   .-   .-.

.-.   .-   .-   —   —
```

```
--- .-- .-. .. - .

-.. --- .-- -. -..-

--- ..- .-. ... .--.

. -.-. .. .- .-.. - ....

--- ..- --. .... - ...

.- -. -.. ..- . . .-..

.. -. --. .-. .-. .-.-.-

.-- .... .- - -.. ---

-.-- --- ..- - -- .. ..
```

My journal of thoughts and feelings

What did you learn today?

Thoughts: DATE

.--- ... .-- — —.. ---

-.-- --- .-- — — .... ..

-. —. ..-. . .—..

-... . .—.. .. . .

.. .-. —.. --- —.

--- — —... . .— .—..

.-. .— .. .—.. —

--- .—. .— .—..

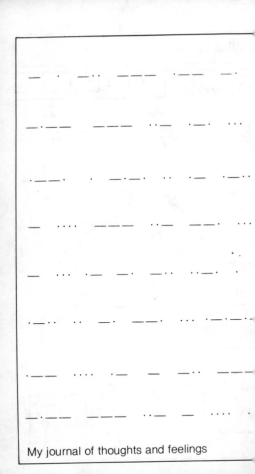

My journal of thoughts and feelings

What is the greatest experience you ever had?

.— ...   .—   —   —..   ———

—.—   ———   .—   —   ...   ..

—.   —.—   ..—.   .   .   .—..

—...   .   .—.   ..   .   ..—   .

..—..   —..   ———   .—.

———   —   .—..   .   .   ..—.

.—.   .   ..   .   —

———   .—.   .—..   ..

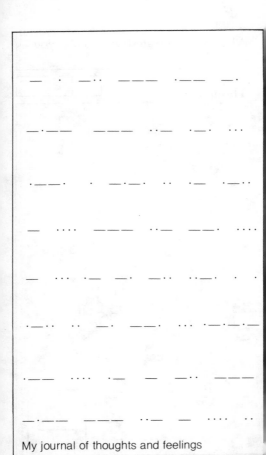

My journal of thoughts and feelings

When it comes down to it, what do
you really believe in?

Thoughts: DATE

.—— ... .— — —.. ———

—.—— ——— ..— — ... ..

—. .—.— ..—. . . .—..

—... .. . .—— .. . ...— .

.. ——.. —.. ——— —.

——— — —..— . .— ..—.

.—. .— — —.. —

——— .—— .—. ..

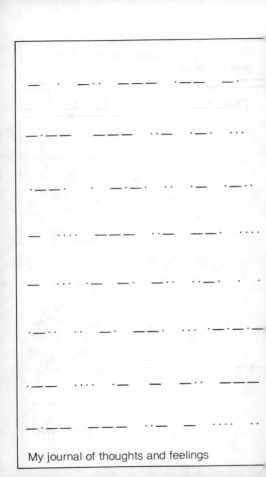

My journal of thoughts and feelings

What kinds of people do you like?

Thoughts: DATE

.___   ...   ._ _   _   _.. ____

_._ _   ___   .._   _   ...   ..

_.   _._   .._.   .   .___ ..

_ ..   .   ._.. .   .   .___ .   .

.. ._.. ..   _._   ___   _.

___   _   _... .   .   .._..

._   ._.   ._.   ..

___   ._ _   ._.   ..

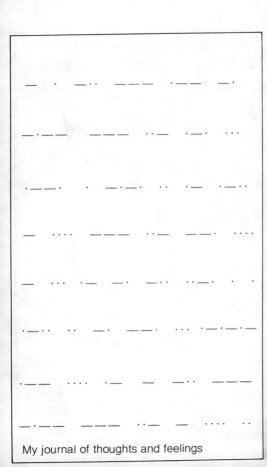

My journal of thoughts and feelings

What do you think about death?

Thoughts: DATE

.___ ... .__ _ _ _.. ___

_.__ ___ ... _ _ .... ..

_. _._ ..._ . . ._..

_... .)_.. . . ..._ .

.._ __.. _.. ___ _.

___ _ _... . ._ .._..

._. ._ .. _.. _

___ ._. ._. ..

My journal of thoughts and feelings

You are a sorcerer and have the power to cast a spell. What words would you use and how would you use the spell?

Thoughts:

.—— ... .— — —.. ———

—.—— ——— ..— — .... ..

—. —.— ..—. . . .—..

—.. . .—.. .. . ..—. .

.. ——.. —.. ——— —.

——— — —.. . .— ..—.

.—.. .— .. —..— —

My journal of thoughts and feelings

What would you change about your parents if you had the power?

Thoughts: DATE

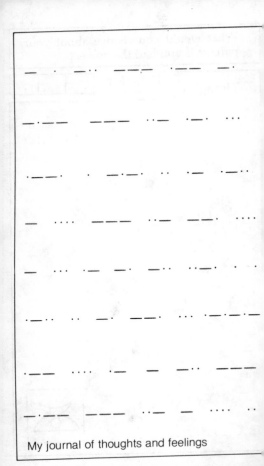

My journal of thoughts and feelings

Once when you were ill and said you
would change if only you would get
well again, what did you mean?

Thoughts:

·—— ··· ·—— — —·· ———

—·—— ——— ·· — ·· ···· ··

—· —·— ··· · · · ·—··

—··· · ·—— ·· · ··· — ·

·· —·· —·· ——— ··· —·

——— — —·· · · · ··—·

·—· ·—· ·· · ·· —

```
___ .__ .__. .. _ .

_.. ___ .__ _. _._ _

___ .._ ._. ... .__.

. _._._ .. ._ ._.. _ ....

___ ..__ __. .... _ ...

._ _. _.. ..__ . . ._.._

.. _. ___. ... ._._._

.__ .... ._ _ _.. ___

_.__ ___ .._ _ .... ..
```

My journal of thoughts and feelings

What is your favorite character you
have read about in a book or seen in a
play and what makes them so special
to you? How are you like or different
from them?

Thoughts: DATE

.— .... .— — —.. ———

—.—— ——— ..— — ... ..

—. —.— ..—. — . .—..

—... . .—— .. . ...— .

..—.. —.. ——— —.

——— — —.. . .— ..—.

.—. .— .. —.. ——

— — — ·— — — ·— — · ·· — ·

—·· — — — ·—— ·—· —· —·——

— — — ··— — ·—· ··· ·——·

· —·—· ·· ·— ·—·· — ····

— — — ··— — —· ···· — ···

·— —· ·—·· ·—· · · ·——··

·· —· — — —· ··· ·—·—·—

·—— ···· ·— — — —·· — — —

—·—— — — — ··— — ···· ··

My journal of thoughts and feelings

What are the things you can do to enjoy your life more?

Thoughts: DATE

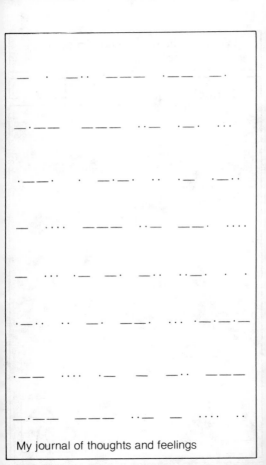

My journal of thoughts and feelings

What is the best thing that could ever
happen to you?

Thoughts: DATE [ ][ ][ ]

.__ ... ._ _ _.. ___

_._ ___ .._ _ ... ..

_. _._ .._ . . ._..

_... . ._.. .. . .

.._.. _.. ___ _.

___ _ _.. . ._ .._

._. ._ .. _.. _

___ ._. ._. ..

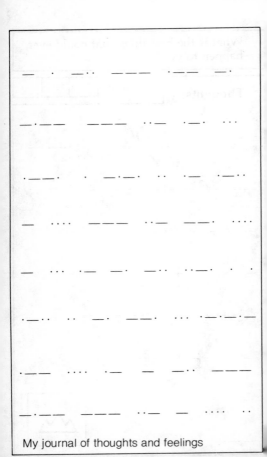

My journal of thoughts and feelings

If you could make a great movie or
write a book, what would it be about?

Thoughts: DATE [ ][ ][ ]

.__ ... ._ _ _.. ___

_.__ ___ .._ _ ... ..

_. .__ .._. . . ._..

_... ._ .__.. .. . ... _ .

.. ___ _.. ___ _.

___ _ ... ._ ._ .._.

._. ._ _ _.. .

___ .__ ._ ._..

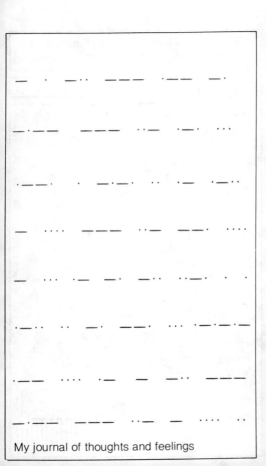

My journal of thoughts and feelings

Thoughts:

.—— ... .— — —.. ———

—.—— ——— ..— — ... ..

—. —.— ..—. . . .—..

—... . .—.— .. . .

..——.. —.. ——— —.

———— —.. . .—.. . . .—.

.—.. —— — .— .. ..

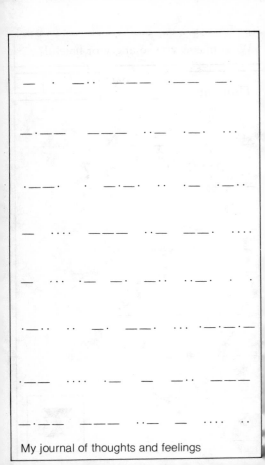

My journal of thoughts and feelings

What are the things you can do to be
less lonely?

Thoughts: DATE [ ][ ][ ]

.— — ... .— — —.. ———

—.— ——— ..— — — ... ..

—. .—. ..—. . .—..

—... . .—.. .. . ...— .

..—.. —.. ——— —.

——— — —.. . .— ..—.

.—. .—. .. —.. —

——— .—— .—. ..

— · —·· ——— ·—— —·

—·—— ——— ··— ·—· ···

·——· · —·—· ·· ·—· ·—··

— ···· ——— ··— —·· ····

— ··· ·— —· —· —· · ·

·—·· ·· —· ——· ··· ·—·—·

·—— ···· ·— — —·· ———

—·—— ——— ··— — ···· ··

My journal of thoughts and feelings

What is your most valuable treasure?
Why is it so?

Thoughts:

___   ...   ._   _   _   _..   ___

_.__   ___   ...   _   _   ...   ..

_.   _._   .._   .   .   ._..

_...   .   .__   ..   .   _   .

..   .._..   _.   ___   _.

___   _   _..   .   .   .._.

._..   .   ._   ..   _..   _

___   .__   ._.   ._.

My journal of thoughts and feelings

How do you like to go "crazy" and have fun?

Thoughts:

.___ ... .__ __ _.. ___

_.__ ___ .__ .. _ ... ..

_. _._ ..._ . . .__..

_.. . ._._ .. . ._..

.. ..__ _.. ___ __..

___ _ _... . ._ .__.

._. ._ __ _... _

___ .__ ._ ._ .__

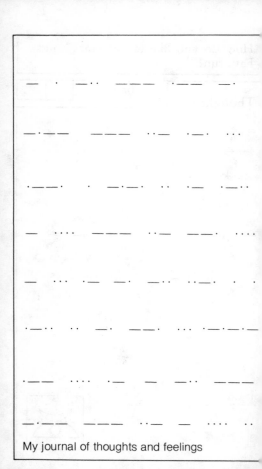

My journal of thoughts and feelings

What are you most afraid of about growing old?

Thoughts:

.___ ... .__ _ _.. ___

_.__ ___ .._ _ ... ..

_. _.. .._. . . ._..

_... . ._.. .. ... .

.._... _.. ___ _.

___ _ _.. . ._ .._.

._. ._ .. _.. ___ ._. .._.

— ·   —·· ——— ·—— —·

—·—— ——— ··— ·—· ···

·——· · —·—· ·· ·— ·—··

— ···· ——— ··— ——· ····

— ··· ·— —· —·· ··—· · ·

·—·· ·· —· ——· ··· ·—·—·—

·—— ···· ·— — —·· ———

—·—— ——— ··— — ···· ··

My journal of thoughts and feelings

Someone has given you a million dollars. What would you do with it?

Thoughts:

.___ ... .__ __ __.. ___

_.__ ___ .._ __ . ... ..

_. _.__ ..__ . . .__..

_.. . .__.. .. . .

.._.__.. _.. ___ __.

___ __ _.. . .__ .._.

._. .__ .. _.. _

___ .__ ._. ..

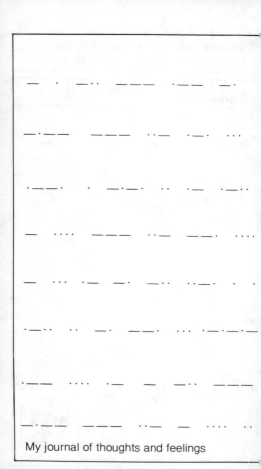

```
—   ·   —··   ———   ·——   —·
—·——   ———   ··—   ·—·   ···
·——·   ·   —·—·   ··   ·—   ·—·
—   ····   ———   ··—   ——·   ····
—   ···   ·—   —·   —··   ··—·   ·   ·
·—··   ··   —·   ——·   ···   ·—·—·
·——   ····   ·—   —   —··   ———
—·——   ———   ··—   —   ····   ··
```

My journal of thoughts and feelings

What new land or place would you like
to go to?

Thoughts:

. __   ...   . _ _ _ _..   ___

_.__ ___ _ .._ _ ... ..

_. _._ ..._ . . ._..

_... . ._ _ .. ... .

.. __.. _.. ___ _.

___ _ _.._ . ._ ._..

._. ._ _.._ _

___ ._. ._. ..

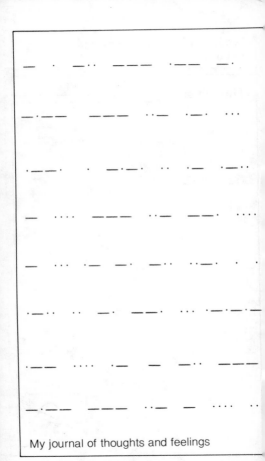

My journal of thoughts and feelings

Were you ever lost? What happened?

Thoughts: DATE [ ][ ][ ]

.__ ... ._ _ _.. ___

_.__ ___ ._ _ ... ..

_. _.. .. . . ._..

_... . ._.. .. . .

.. __.. _.. ___ _.

___ _ _.. . ._ __.

._ ._ _.. .

___ ._.. ._ .. ..

— · —·· ——— ·—— —·

·—— ——— ··— ·—· ···

·——· · —·—· ·· ·— ·—··

— ···· ——— ··— ——· ····

— ··· ·— —· —·· ··— · ·

·—·· ·· —· ——· ··· ·—· ·—·—·—

·—— ···· ·— — —·· ———

—·—— ——— ··— — ···· ··

My journal of thoughts and feelings

If you could use your imagination to
get back at someone who hurt you,
what would you do to them?

Thoughts: DATE [ ][ ][ ]

.—— ... .— — — —.. ———

—.—— ——— ..— — . ... ..

—. —.— ..—. . . .—..

—... . .—.. .. . . ..—. .

.. ——.. —.. ——— —.

——— — —.. . .— ..—.

.—. . .— .. —.. —

```
---   ·--   ·-·   ··   -   ·

-··   ---   ·--   -·   -·--

---   ··-   ·-·   ···   ·--·

·   -·-·   ··   ·-   ·-··   -   ····

---   ··-   --·   ····   -   ···

·-   -·   -··   ··-·   ·   ·   ·-··

··   -·   --·   ···   ·-·-·

·--   ····   ·-   -   ·   -··   ---

-·--   ---   ··-   -   -   ···   ··
```

My journal of thoughts and feelings

What new thing did you notice today?

Thoughts:

DATE

.－－ ... .－ － －.. －－－

－.－－ －－－ .. － ... ..

－. －.－ ..－. . . .－..

－... . .－.. .. . ...－ .

.. －－．.. －.. －－－ －.

－－－ － －... . . ..－

.－. .－ .－ －.. ..

－－－ .－－ .－. ..

— ·   —··   ———   ·——   —·

—·—   ———   ··—   ·—·   ···

·——·   ·   —·—·   ··   ·—   ·—··

—   ····   ———   ·—   ——·   ····

—   ···   ·—   —·   —·   ··—·   ·   ·

·—··   ··   —·   ——·   ···   ·—·—·—

·——   ····   ·—   —   —··   ———

—·——   ———   ··—   —   ····   ··

My journal of thoughts and feelings

If you could be a flower, what would you be?

Thoughts:

.___ ... ._ _ _.. ___

_.__ ___ .._ _ ... ..

_. _.._ ... ._ _...

_... . ._.. .. . .

.._.. _. ___ _.

___ _ _... . ._ ..._

._. . .._ _ ._ ..._

___ ._.. .._ _...

— · —·· ——— ·—— —·

·—— ——— ··— ·—· ···

·——· · —·—· ·· ·— ·—··

— ···· ——— ··— ——· ····

— ··· ·— —· —·· ··— · ·

·—·· ··· —· ——· ··· ·—·—·—

·—— ··· ·— — —·· ———

—·—— ——— ··— — ···· ··

My journal of thoughts and feelings

What is your saddest memory?

Thoughts: DATE [ ][ ][ ]

.— ... .— — —.. ———

—.—— ——— ..— — ... ..

—. —.— ..—. . . .—..

—... . .—.. .. —

.. ——.. —.. ——— —.

——— — —... . .— ..—.

.—. .— .—. ..

——— .—. .—. ..

My journal of thoughts and feelings

What is the hardest riddle you know?

Thoughts:

My journal of thoughts and feelings

Have you ever frightened someone or
hurt them? What did you do to them?
Why?

Thoughts: DATE [ ][ ][ ]

.—— ... .— — —.. ———

—.—— ——— ..— — ... ..

—. —.— ..—. . . .—..

....—— .. . .

.. —.. —.. ——— —.

——— — —.. . . .—..

.—. .—.—.— — .—.. . .—..

——— .—— .— .. .. ..

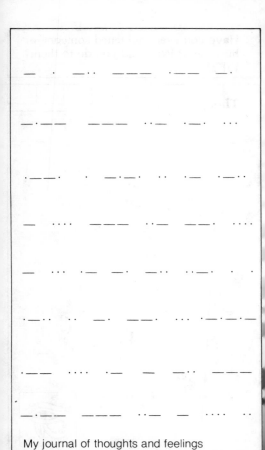

My journal of thoughts and feelings

If you could be a toy, what would you be?

.__ ... ._ _ _ _.. ____

_.__ ___ .._ _ _ ... ..

_. _._ .._ . . ._..

_... . ._.. . ... .

.. __.. _.. ___ _.

___ _ _... . . ...

._. _._ _ _

___ ._.. .._. ..

My journal of thoughts and feelings

What are the things you don't like in
other people?

.—— ... .— — —.. ———

—.—— ——— ..— — ... ..

—. —.— ..—. . . .—..

—... . .—— .. . .

..—.. —.. ——— —.

——— — —.. . .— ..—.

—. .— .. —.. —

——— .—— .—. ..

```
—  ·  —··  ———  ·——  —·

—·——  ———  ··—  ·—·  ···

·——·  ·  —·—  ··  ·—  ·—··

—  ····  ———  ·—  ——·  ····

—  ···  ·—  —·  —··  ··—·  ·  ·

·—··  ··  —·  ——·  ···  ·—·—·

·——  ····  ·—  —  —··  ———

—·——  ———  ··—  —  ····  ··
```

My journal of thoughts and feelings

In all of language, what is the most beautiful word you know?

What about some word that does not yet exist?

.— ... .— — —.. ———

—.— ——— ..— — ... ..

—. —.— ..— . . .—..

—... . .—.. .. . ..— .

.. ——.. —.. ——— —.

——— — —.. . .— .. ..—

.—. .— .. —.. —

‑‑‑ ·‑‑ ·‑· ·· ‑ ·

‑·· ‑‑‑ ·‑‑ ‑· ‑·‑‑

‑‑‑ ··‑ ·‑· ··· ·‑‑·

· ‑·‑· ·· ·‑ ·‑·· ‑ ····

‑‑‑ ··‑ ‑‑· ···· ‑ ···

·‑ ‑· ‑·· ··‑· · · ·‑··

·· ‑· ‑‑· ··· ·‑·‑·‑

·‑‑ ···· ·‑ ‑ ‑·· ‑‑‑

‑·‑‑ ‑‑‑ ··‑ ‑ ··· ··

My journal of thoughts and feelings

When are the times you feel most like hiding? Where would you like to go at these times?

.___ . . . .__ _ _.. ___

_.__ ___ .. _ _ ... ..

_. _._ .. _. . . ._..

_... . ._.. .. . ..._ .

.. __.. _.. ___ _.

___ _ _... . ._ .._.

._. ._ .. _.. _

```
--- .-- .-. .. - .

-.. --- .-- -. -.--

--- .- .-. ... .--.

. -.-. .. .- .-. - ....

--- .- --. .... - ...

.- -.- -.. ..- . . .-..

.. -. --. ... .-.-.

.-- .... .- - - -.. ---

-.-- --- ..- - .... ..
```

My journal of thoughts and feelings

How did you learn to stand on your own two feet?

Thoughts: DATE

.-- ... .- - -.. ---

_.-- --- ..- .- .... ..

-. --- ..- .- . . -..

-... . .--- .. . .

..-. -.. --- --- -.

--- - -..- . .- ..-.

.-. .-. - -

--- .-- .- ..

— · —·· ——— ·—— —·

—·—— ——— ··— ·—· ···

·——· · —·—· ·· ·— ·—··

— ···· ——— ·· ——· ····

— ·· ·— —· —·· ··— · · ·

·—·· ·· —· ——· ··· ·—·—·

·—— ···· ·— — —· —·· ———

—·—— ——— ··— — ···· ··

My journal of thoughts and feelings

If you were to tell the tale of your life to someone, in a way no one would know it's you, what would your story be?

Thoughts:

DATE

.__ ... .__ _ _ _.. ___

_.__ ___ .._ _ ... ..

_. _._ .._. . . ._..

_.._ . ._.. .. . .

.. __.. _.. ___ _.

___ _ _.. . ._ .._.

._. ._ .. _.. _

My journal of thoughts and feelings

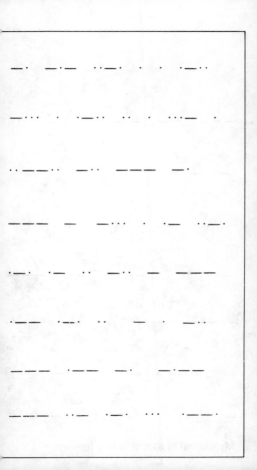

· —·—· ·· ·— ·—·· — ····

——— ··— ——· ···· — ···

·— —· —·· ··—· · · ·—··

·· —· ——· ··· ·—·—·—

·—— ···· ·— — —·· ———

—·—— ——— ··— — ···· ···

—· —·— ··—· · · ·—··

—··· · ·—·· ·· · ···— ·

My journal of thoughts and feelings

What is the way you like love to be shown to you? How do you show love?

Thoughts:

.__ ... .__ _ _ _.. ___

_.__ ___ .._ _ ... ..

_. _._ ..__. . . ._..

_.. . ._.. .. . ..._ .

.. __.. _.. ___ _.

___ _ _.. . ._ .._.

._. ._ .. _.. _

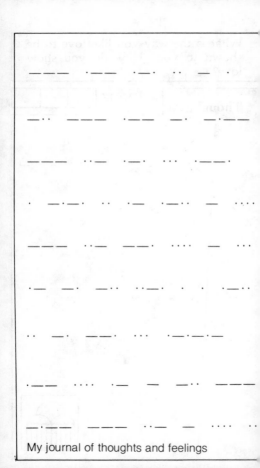

My journal of thoughts and feelings

What makes you cry?

Thoughts:

.--- .... .-- - -.. ---

-.-- --- .. - .... ..

-. -.- .-. . .-..

-.. . .-.- . ... -.

.. --. .-- --- --.

--- - .-. . -. ..-

.-. .-. .. .-.- .-

--- .-- .-.

```
—   ·   —··   ———   ·——   —·

—·——   ———   ··—   ·—·   ···

·——·   ·   —·—·   ··   ·—   ·—·

—   ····   ———   ··—   ——·   ····

—   ···   ·—   —·   —··   ··—·   ·   ·   ·

·—··   ··   —·   ——·   ···   ·—·—·—

·——   ····   ·—   —   —··   ———

—·——   ———   ··—   —   ····   ··
```

My journal of thoughts and feelings

What is your favorite work of art?
What does it do for you?

Thoughts:

DATE

.__ ... .__ __ _.. ___

_.__ ___ ..__ __ ... ..

_. _._ .._. . . ._..

_.. . ._.. .. . .

.._ __ _.. ___ __.

___ _ _.. . . .._

._. . _ .. _

___ .__ ._. .

— · —·· ——— ·—— —·

—·—— ——— ··— ·—· ···

·——· · —·—· ·· ·— ·—··

— ···· ——— ··— ——· ····

— ··· ·— —· —·· ··—· ·

·—·· ·· —· ——· ··· ·—·—·

·—— ···· ·— — —·· ———

—·—— ——— ··— · ···· ··

My journal of thoughts and feelings

What are some things you were once
afraid of, but are no longer?

Thoughts: DATE

.__ ... ._ _ _.. ___

_.__ ___ .__ .._ _ ... ..

_. ._._ .._. . . ._..

_... . ._.. .. . .

.. __.. _.. ___ _.

___ _ _.. .._ ._ .._.

._. ._ .. _.. _

___ .__ .._ ._.

My journal of thoughts and feelings

If you were going to a masked ball and could find a costume to match your wildest dreams, how would you look? Describe it or draw it so you won't forget.

Thoughts: DATE

My journal of thoughts and feelings

What big problems are you struggling with? What big problems did you have a year ago, and how did you solve them?

Thoughts:

._ __ ... ._ _ _.. ___

_.__ ___ .. _ ... ..

_. _._ .._. . ._..

_.. . ._.. . ... _ .

..__.. _.. ___ _.

___ _ _.. . ._ .__.

._. ._ _ ._.. _

___ .__ ._. ..

— · —·· ——— ·—— —·

—·—— ——— ··— ·—· ···

·——· · —·—· ·· ·— ·—··

— ···· ——— ··— ——· ····

— ··· ·— —· —·· ··—· · ·

·—·· ·· —· ——· ···

·—— ···· ·— — —·· ———

—·—— ——— ··— — ···· ··

My journal of thoughts and feelings

What kind of invention would you like
to invent? What would it do?

Thoughts: DATE

.__ ... .__ _ _ _.. ___

_.__ ___ .._ _ ___ .._ ... ..

_. _.. .._. . . ._..

_... . ...

.. .__ _.. ___ _ _.

___ .__ _ .._ . ._ ..._

._. .__ _

___ .__ ._ ._

```
—  ·   —··   ·   —··   ·——·

—  ·——  ———   ———  ··  ·—·  ···

·——·  ·  —·—·  ··  ·—  ·—·

—  ···   ———  ··  —·  ·

—  ···  ·—  —·  —··  ··  ·  ·

·—·  ··  ·  —  ——·  ···  ·——·—

·——  ····  ·—  —  —  ··  ———

—·——  ———  ··  —  ····  ··
```

My journal of thoughts and feelings

When are the times you feel most`lost and lonely?

Thoughts: DATE ☐ ☐ ☐

.—— ... .— — —.. ———

—.—— ——— ..— — .... ..

—. —.— .. . . .—..

—... . .—. .. . .

.. .—.. —.. ——— —.

———— — —.. . .— ..—.

.—. .. .. — .—..

——— .—. .— .. ..

— ·   —··   ———   ·——   —·

—·——   ———   ··—   ·—·   ···

·——·   ·   —·—·   ··   ·—   ·—··

—   ····   ———   ··—   ——·   ····

—   ···   ·—   —   —·   ··—·   ·   ·

·—··   ··   —·   ——·   ···   ·—·—·—

·——   ····   ·—   —   —··   ———

—·——   ———   ··—   —   ····   ··

My journal of thoughts and feelings

What kind of person do you want to
be? How, if at all, would you change?

.__ ... .__ _ _.. ___

_.__ ___ .._ __ _ ... ..

_. .._ ._ _ . . ._..

_.. .. . ._.. .. ..

.._.. _.. _ ___ _.

___ _ _.._ . ._ ..._.

._. ._ .. _.. _

___ ... ._.. ..

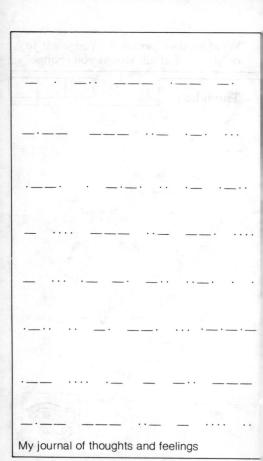

My journal of thoughts and feelings

What are the things you want to tell a
child to help them along in life?

Thoughts:

.── ... .─ ─ ─.. ───

─.── ─── ..─ ─ ... ..

─. ─.─ ..─. . .─..

─.. . .── .. . .

.. ──.. ─.. ─── ─.

.── ─ ─.── . .─ ..─.

.─. .─ .. ─.. ─

─── .── ─.─ ..

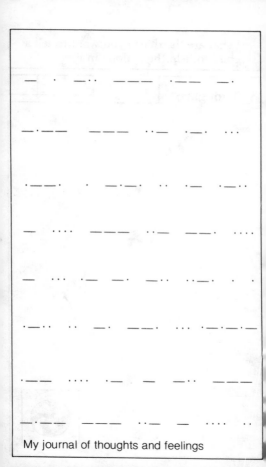

My journal of thoughts and feelings

What new discovery do you want to
make?

Thoughts: DATE

.___   ...   ._   _   _..   ___

_.__   ___   .._   _   ...   ..

_.   _._   .._.   .   .   ._..

_...   .   ._..   ..   .   .

..___..   _..   ___   _.

___   _   _...   .   ._   .._.

._.   ._   ..   _.._   _

___   ._.   ._.   ..

— · —·· ——— ·—— —·

—·—— ——— ··— ·—· ···

·——· · —·—· ·· ·— ·—··

— ··· ——— ·— ——· ····

— ··· ·— —· —·· ··— · ·

·—·· ·· —· ——· ··· ·—·—·—

·—— ···· ·— — —·· ———

—·—— ——— ··— — ···· ··

My journal of thoughts and feelings

Whom do you admire? Why?

Thoughts: 　　DATE ☐ ☐ ☐

```
.__  ...  ._  _  _..  ___

_.__  ___  .__  ._  _  ...  ..

_.  ._  __  .._.  .  ._  ._..

_..  ._..  ._  _  ___  .

..  .__  _..  ___  _  _.

___  _  _..  .  ._  .._.

._.  ..  ._  ..  _

___  .__  ._  ..
```

My journal of thoughts and feelings

What bitterness do you have in your soul?

.-- .... .- - -.. ---

-.-- --- ..- - .... ..

-. -.- ..-. . . .-..

-... . .-.. .. . ...- .

.. ..-. -.. --- -.

--- - -.. - .- ..-.

.-. .- .. -.. -

--- ..- .- .-. ..

— · —·· ——— ·—— —·

—·—— ——— ··— ·—· ···

·——· · —·—· ·· ·— ·—··

— ···· ——— ··— ——·· ····

— ··· ·— —· ·—· ··· ·

·—·· ·· —· ——· ··· ·—·—·—

·—— ···· ·— — —·· ———

—·—— ——— ··— — · ···· ··

My journal of thoughts and feelings

Tell me a great joke.

− · −·· −−− ·−− −·

−·−− −−− ··− ·−· ···

·−−· · −·−· ·· ·− ·−··

− ···· −−− ··− −−· ····

− ··· ·− −· −·· ··− · ·

·−·· ·· −· −−· ·−·−·−

·−− ··· ·− − −·· −−−

−·−− −−− ··− − ···· ··

My journal of thoughts and feelings

What are the things that make you feel more powerful in life? What would you do with more power?

Thoughts:
DATE

.___   ...   .__   _   _..   ___

_.__   ___   .._   _   ...   ..

_.   _._   .._.   .   .   _..

_..   .   ._.   .   .   ...   .

.._.._..   _..   ___   _.

___   _   _...   .   ._   .._

._.   ._   ..   _..   _

\--- .\--- .\-. .. \- .

\-.. \--- .\-- \-. \-.\--

\--- ..\- .\-. ... .\--.

. \-.\-. .. .\- .\-.. \- ...

\--- ..\- \--\-. .... \- ...

.\-- \-. \-.. ..\-. . .\-..

.. \-. \--. ... .\-.\-.\-

.\-- .... .\- \- \-.. \---

\-.\-- \--- ..\- \- .... ..

My journal of thoughts and feelings

What has been the hardest thing you have had to do so far in your life? And how did you do it?

Thoughts: DATE [ ][ ][ ]

.__   ...   ._   _   _..   ___

_.__   ___   .._   _   ...   ..

_.   _._   .._   .   ._..

_...   .   ._..   ..   .   .

.._..   _..   ___   _.

___   _   _..   .   ._   ._..

._.   ._   ..   _..   _

My journal of thoughts and feelings

What is the question you're afraid to
ask yourself?

Thoughts: DATE

.—— ... .— — —.. ———

—.—— ——— ..— — .... ..

—. .—— ..— . . .—..

—... . .—— .. . ...

..—— —.. ——— —.

——— — —... . .— .—..

.—. .— .. .—.. —

——— .—— .— ..

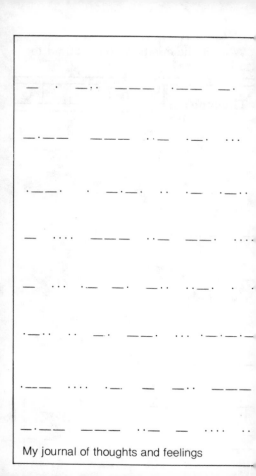

My journal of thoughts and feelings

What's the funniest thing that ever
happened to you?

Thoughts:

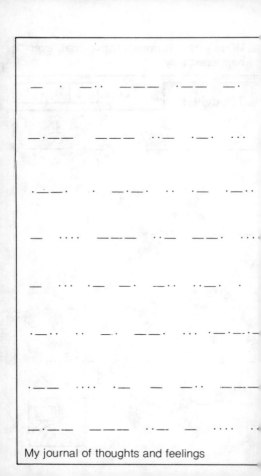

— · —·· ——— ·—— —·

—·—— ——— ·· — ·—· ···

·——· · —·—· ·· ·— ·—··

— ···· ——— ·· — ——· ···

— ··· ·— —· —·· ··—· ·

·—·· ·· —· ——· ··· ·—·—·—

·—— ··· ·— — —·· ——·

—·—— ——— ··— — ···· ··

My journal of thoughts and feelings

What was your most marvelous dream?

Thoughts: DATE

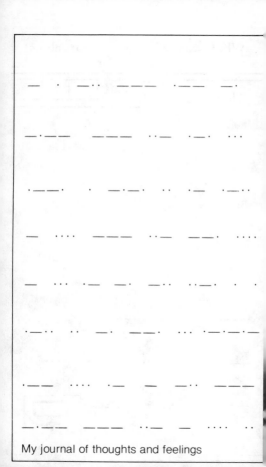

My journal of thoughts and feelings

What was the most difficult time you had to get over?

Thoughts:

DATE

.—— ... .— — —.. ———

—.—— ——— ..— — ... ..

—. —.— ..—. . . .—..

—... . .—.. . . ... —.

..—.. —.. ——— —.

——— — —... . .— ..—.

.—. .— .. .—.. —

——— .—— .—. ..

My journal of thoughts and feelings

Could you write something in a secret language that no else could figure out? (Please write the translation upside down someplace on this page or the next one just in case you forget what the words or sounds mean.)

Thoughts:

DATE | | |

My journal of thoughts and feelings

What's getting in your way?

Thoughts: DATE

.___ ...   .__ _   _.._   ___

_.___   _ ___   .._ _   ...   ..

_. _.._   ..__. . .   ._.._

_...   .   ._._   .. . .._.   .

..   _._   ___ _.

___   _   _.._   .   ._   ._._.

._._   ._   ._._.   ..

___   .__   ._._   ..

My journal of thoughts and feelings

If you could be a smell, what would you be?

If you could be a monster, what would you be like?

Thoughts:

DATE | | |

.__ ... ._ _ _.. ___

_.__ ___ ._. _ ... ..

_. _._ ... . . ._..

_... . ,_.. .. . ..._ .

..__.. _.. ___ _.

___ _ _... . ._ ._..

._. ._ .. _.. _

−−− ·−− ·−·· ·· −·

−·· −−− ·−− −· −·−−

−−− ··− ·−· ··· ·−−·

· −·−· ·· ·−− ·−·· −·· ····

−−− ··− −−· ···· −· ···

·− −·· −·· ·· ·· · · ·−··

·· −·· −−· ··· ·−·−·−

·−− ···· ·− −· −·· −−−

−·−− −−− ··− −· · ···· ··

My journal of thoughts and feelings

What are the things you like about yourself? What's good about you?

Thoughts:

DATE

.—— ... .— — —.. ———

—.—— ——— ..— — ... ..

—. —.—. .— —. . . .—..

—... . .—.— . . ..

.. .———. . —. ——— —.

——— — ... . .— ..—..

.—. .— .. —. . .—.

My journal of thoughts and feelings

What do you expect from death?

Thoughts: DATE [ ][ ][ ]

·— — ··· ·— — — —·· ———

—·— ——— ··— — ··· ··

—· ·—· ··—· · · ·—··

—·· · ·—·· · · ··· ·

·· ——·· —·· ——— —·

——— — —··· · — ··—

·—· · —·· ·· — —

——— ·—— ·—· ·

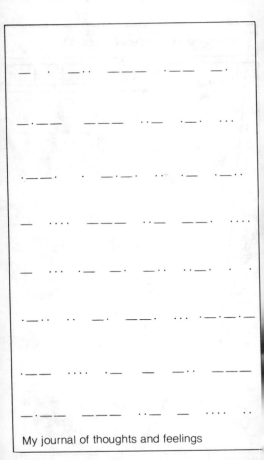

My journal of thoughts and feelings

What kind of hero or heroine would
you want to be?

Thoughts:

.__ ... ._ _ _ _.. ___

_.__ ___ .._ _ ... ..

_. _._ .._. . . ._._..

_.. . .__ .. . .

.. __ _.. ___ __.

___ _ _.. . ._ .._.

._. ._ _ _

___ .__ ._. ..

—· —·· ——— ·—— —·

—·—— ——— ··— ·—· ···

·——· · —·—· ·· ·— ·—··

— ···· ——— ··— ——· ····

— ··· ·— —· —·· ··—· · ·

·—·· ·· —· ——· ··· ·—·—·—

·—— ···· ·— — —·· ———

—·—— ——— ··— — ···· ··

My journal of thoughts and feelings

What are some of the things that still
frighten you? How can you fight back?

Thoughts: DATE

._ _   ....   ._   _   _..   _ _ _

_._ _   _ _ _   .._   _   ....   ..

_.   _._   .._.   .   .   ._..

_...   .   ._..   ..   .   ._   .

..   _ _..   _..   _ _ _   _ _.

_ _ _   _   _...   .   ._   .._.

._.   ._   ..   _..   _

_ _ _   ._ _   ._.   ..

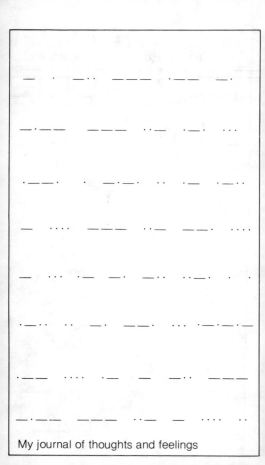

My journal of thoughts and feelings

What do you hate most?

Thoughts: DATE

```
.——    ...    .—    —    —..    ———

—.——    ———    ..—    —    ...    ..

—.    —.—    ..—.    .    .    .—..

—...    .    .—..    ..    .    ...—    .

..    ——..    —..    ———    —.

———    —..—    .    .—    ..—.

.—.    .    —..    —..    —

———    .—    .—.    ..
```

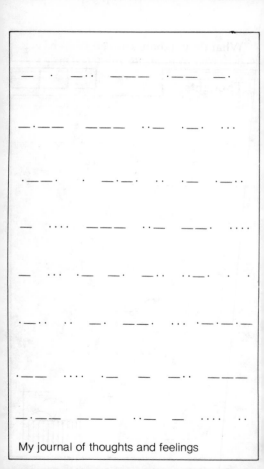

My journal of thoughts and feelings

What are some things you have achieved in your life so far?

Thoughts: DATE

— · —·· ——— ·—— —·

—·—— ——— ··— ·—· ···

·——· · —·—· ·· ·— ·—··

— ···· ——— ··— ——· ····

— ··· ·— —· —·· ··—· · ·

·—·· ·· —· ——· ··· ·—·—·—

·—— ···· ·— — —·· ———

—·—— ——— ··— — ···· ··

My journal of thoughts and feelings

What have you learned from your mis-
takes?

Thoughts:

.—— ... .— — —·· ———

_.—— ——— ..— — ... ..

_. —.— ..— . . ._··

_... . .—— .. . .

.._·· _.. ——— —·

——— — _·· . . ._·—

._. .—— —

——— .—— ._. ..

‑ ·   ‑·· ‑‑‑ ·‑‑ ‑·

‑·‑‑ ‑‑‑ ··‑ ·‑· ···

·‑‑· ·   ‑·‑· ·· ·‑ ·‑··

‑ ····   ‑‑‑‑ ·‑   ‑‑‑· ····

‑ ···   ·‑ ‑·   ‑·· ··‑·   ·   ·

·‑·· ··   ‑· ‑‑·   ·   ·‑·‑·‑

·‑‑ ····   ·‑ ‑ ‑··   ‑‑‑

‑·‑‑ ‑‑‑ ··‑ ‑ ····   ··

My journal of thoughts and feelings

If you could step outside your body to see yourself clearly, what kind of person would you see? How would you like to be?

Thoughts:

DATE

.── ... .─ ─ ─.. ───

─.── ──── ─ ..─ ─ ─ .... ..

─. ─.─ ..─.─ . . .─..

─.. . .─.. .. . ...─. .

..──.. ─.. ─── ─.

─── ─ ─.. . .─ .──.

.─. . .─ .. ─. ─

─── .─. .─. ..

My journal of thoughts and feelings

What was the saddest time in your life?

Thoughts: DATE [ ][ ][ ]

.‒‒   ...   .‒   ‒   ‒..   ‒‒‒

‒.‒‒   ‒‒‒   ..‒   ‒   ...   ..

‒.   ‒.‒   ..‒.   .   .   .‒..

‒...   .   .‒.   ‒   .   ...   .

..   .‒‒..   ‒..   ‒‒‒   ‒.

‒‒‒   ‒   ‒...   .   .‒   ..‒.

.‒.   .‒   ..   .‒..   ‒

‒‒‒   .‒‒.   .‒.   ..

My journal of thoughts and feelings

What name would you choose if you
could name yourself? Why this name?
Does it have a meaning?

Thoughts: DATE [ ][ ][ ]

.__ ... .__ _ _.. ___

_.__ ___ ._ _ ... ..

_. _._ .._. . ._..

_.. _._ .. . .

.._.. _.. ___ _.

___ _ _.. . ._ .._.

._. ._ .. _.. _

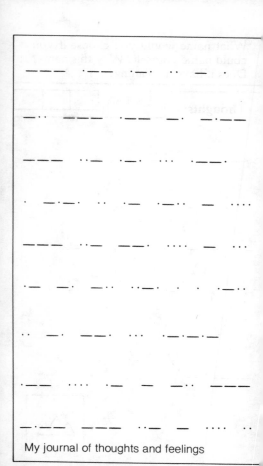

My journal of thoughts and feelings

What cares would you wish to drop?

Thoughts: DATE

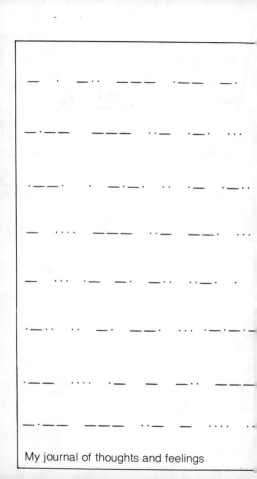

My journal of thoughts and feelings

What are the things about your parents or someone close to you that worry you?

Thoughts: DATE [ ][ ][ ]

.__ ... ._ _ _.. ___

_.__ ___ .._ _ .... ..

_. _._ .._ . . ._.

_.. . ._. .. . .

.. ___.. _. ___ _.

___ _ _.. . ._ .._.

._. ._ .. _. _

___ ._. .. ..

My journal of thoughts and feelings

If you could be different, how would you be?

Thoughts: DATE [ ][ ][ ]

.__ ... ._ _ _.. ___

_.__ ___ .._ _ ... ..

_. _._ .._ . . ._..

_... . .__.. .. . ..._ .

.. __.. _.. ___ __ _.

___ _ __.. . ._ .._.

._. ._ .. _.. _

___ __ ._. _.

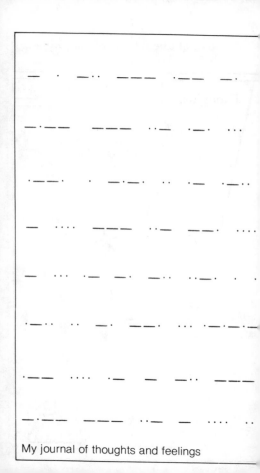

My journal of thoughts and feelings

What are the things you want to learn?

Thoughts:
DATE

.-- ... .- - -.. ---

-.-- --- ..- - .... ..

-. -.- ..- . . .-..

-... . .-.. .. ... .

.. --.. -.. --- --.

--- - -.. . .- ..-.

.-. .- .. -.. -

--- .-. .-. ..

— · —·· ——— ·—— —·

—·—— ——— ··— ·—· ···

·——·· · —·—· ·· ·— ·—··

— ···· ——— ··— ——· ····

— ··· ·— —· —·· ··—· · ·

·—·· ·· — ——· ··· ·—·—·—

·—— ···· ·— — —·· ———

—·—— ——— ··— — ···· ··

My journal of thoughts and feelings

What makes you sad?

Thoughts: DATE

.— — ... .— — —.. ——

—.— —— ..— — ... ..

—. .— ..—. . .—..

—... . .—.. . ...— .

.. —.. ——— —.

——— — —... . ..—

.—. — .. .— —

—— .—. .—. ..

— · —·· ——— ·—— —·

—·— ——— ··— ·—· ···

·——· · —·—· ·· ·— ·—··

— ···· ——— ··— ——· ····

— ··· ·— —· —·· ··—· · ·

·—·· ·· —· ——· ··· ·—·—·—

·—— ···· ·— — —·· ———

—·—— ——— ··— — ···· ··

My journal of thoughts and feelings

What are your hopes in life?

Thoughts: DATE [ ][ ][ ]

.—— ...   .— —   —·· ———

—·—— ———   ··— —   —   ···   ··

—·   —·— ··—   ·   ·   ·—·

—··   ·   ·—— —   ·   ···— ·

·· ——··   —·   ——— —·

——— — —··   ·   ·— —   ··—·

·—· ·— ·· — —· ·—

———— ·—— ·—   ··

— · —·· ——— ·—— —·

—·—— ——— ··— ·—· ···

·——· · —·—· ·· ·— ·—·

— ···· ——— ··— ——· ····

— ··· ·— —· —·· ·—· · ·

·—·· ·· —· ——· ··· ·—·—·

·—— ···· ·— — —·· ———

—·—— ——— ··— — ···· ··

My journal of thoughts and feelings

What strange adventure would you like to have?

Thoughts: DATE ☐☐☐

.-- ... .-- -- -.. ---

-.-- -- -- - ... ..

-. -.-- ..-. . . .--..

-... . .-.. . ... .

..-.. -.. --- -.

--- - -... . .- ..-.

.-. .- -.. -

--- .-- .-. ..

— · —·· ——— ·—— —·

—·— ——— ··— ·—· ···

·——· · —·—· ·· ·— —··

— ···· ——— ··— ——· ····

— ··· ·— —· —·· ··—· · ·

·—·· ·· —· ——· ··· ·—·—·

·—— ···· ·— — —·· ———

—·—· ——— ··— — ···· ··

My journal of thoughts and feelings

What is your favorite doodle?

Thoughts: DATE

My journal of thoughts and feelings

What is there in you that you take pride in?

Thoughts:

```
.__   ...   ._   _   _..   ___

_.__   ___   .._   _   ...   ..

_.   _._   .._.   .   .   ._..

_..   .   ._..   ..   .   ..._   .

.._   _..   ___   _..

___   _   _..   .   ._   .._.

._   ._   ..   _..   _

___   .__   ._.._
```

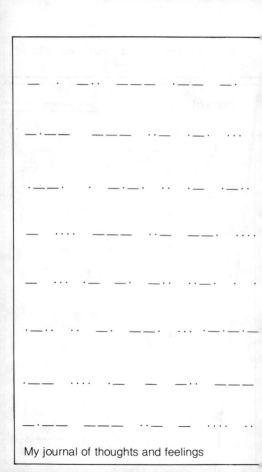

My journal of thoughts and feelings

If you could be a color, what would you be? (Put it on this page to see.)

Thoughts: DATE

My journal of thoughts and feelings

What will be the next milestone in your life?

Thoughts: DATE ☐ ☐ ☐

.___ ... ._ _ _.. ___

_.__ ___ ... _ _ ... ..

_. ._. _ ... . . ._..

_.. . ._ .. .. _ .

.. ._ _.. ___ _.

___ _ _.. . ._ ..._

._. ._ .. .._..

___ ._. ._ ..

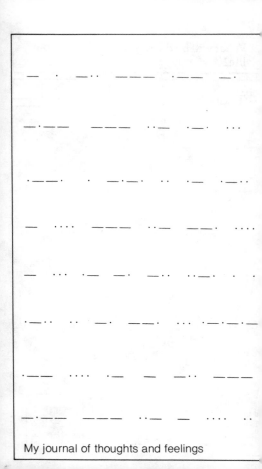

— · —·· ——— ·—— —·

—·—— ——— ··— ·—· ···

·——· · —·—· ·· ·— ·—··

— ···· ——— ··— ——· ····

— ··· ·— —· —·· ··—· · ·

·—·· ·· —· ——· ··· ·—·—·—

·—— ···· ·— — —·· ———

—·—— ——— ··— — ···· ··

My journal of thoughts and feelings

What was the most wonderful thing that ever happened to you?

Thoughts: DATE

·−− ··· ·−− − − −·· −−−

−·−− −−− ·· − − ··· ··

−· −·− ·−− · ·−··

−·· · ·−·· · ··· ·

·· −−·· −·· −−− −·

−−− − −··· · ·− ··−·

·−· ·· −− −

−−− ·−− ·−· ··

My journal of thoughts and feelings

Who touched you today?

Thoughts: DATE ☐ ☐ ☐

.___ ... .__ __ __.. ___

_.___ ___ .._ _ ... ..

_. _._ .._ . ._..

_... . _.._ .. . .

.._ _.._ _._ ___ __.

___ __ _.._ . _._ ._._

._. ._ .. _.._ _

____ .__ .._ ..

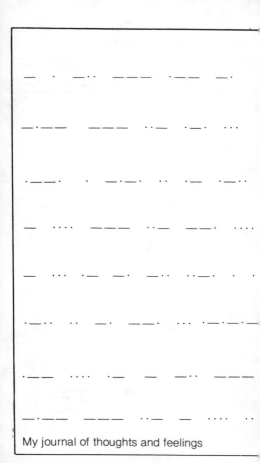

My journal of thoughts and feelings

What truth have you learned you want to share?

Thoughts:

·—— ··· ·— — —·· ———

—·— ——— ··— — ···· ··

—· —·— ··—· · · ·—··

—·· · ·—— ·· · ···— ·

··——·· —·· ——— —·

——— — —··· · ·— ·—·

·—· ·· —·— —

——— ·—— ·—·· ··

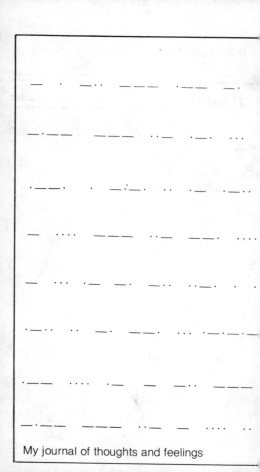

My journal of thoughts and feelings

If you could be a sound, what would you be?

Thoughts: DATE [ ][ ][ ]

.___   ...   .__   _   _..   ___

_.__   ___   ...   _   ....   ..

_.   .   .__   .._.   .   .   ._.

_...   .   ._.__   ..__.   .   .   ...   .

..___   .   ._.__   _..   ___   _.

___   _   _.._   .   .   .   ._.

._.   ._   ..   _   ..   _

___   ._.   ._   ._   ..

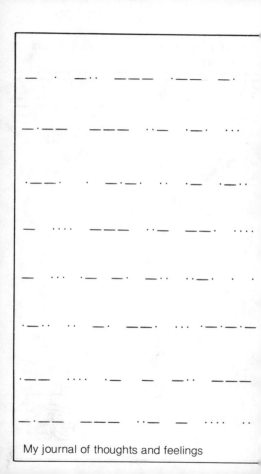

My journal of thoughts and feelings

If you could write a poem or sing a song, what would it be? How would it go?

.___   ...   .__   _   _   _..   ___

_.__   ___   .._   _   ...   ..

_.   _._   .._   .   ._..

_..   .   .___   ..   .   ..._   .

.._..   _..   ___   _.

___   _   _...   .   ._   .__.

._.   ._   .._   _..   _

```
--- .-- .-. .. - .

-.. --- .-- -. -.--

--- ..- .-. ... .-.

. -.-. .. .- .-.. - ...

--- ..- --. - .... - ...

.- -. -.. ..- . . .-..

.. -. --. . ... .-.-.-

.-- ... .- - -.. ..- ---

-.-- --- ..- - . .... ..
```

My journal of thoughts and feelings

Thoughts: DATE

.___   ...   .__   _   _   _..   ___

_.__   ___   __   .__   _   ...   ..

_.   _._   ._..   .   .   _   _..

_...   .   ._..   .   .   .._   .

..   _..   _..   ___   _.

___   _   _..   .__   ._   ._..

._..   .   .___   ._   ._..

___   .__   ._..   ._   ..

— ·   —·· ——— ·—— —·

·—— ——— ··— ·—· ···

·——· ·   —·—· ·· ·— ·—··

— ····   ——— — ··—   ——· ····

— ···   ·— —·   —·· ··—· ·   ··

·—·· ··   —· ——·   ···   ·—·—·—

·—— ····   ·— — —··   ———

—·—— ——— ··— — ····   ··

My journal of thoughts and feelings

What funny or puzzling story have you heard lately?

Thoughts: DATE

.___ ... .__ _ _ _.. ___

_.__ ___ .._ _ ... ..

_. _._ ..._ . . ._..

_... . ._.. .. . ._ .

.._.. _.. ___ _.

___ _ _.._ . ._ .._.

._. ._ .. _.. _

___ ._. ._. ..

—· · —·· ——— ·—— —·

—·— ——— ··— ·—· ···

·——· · —·—· ·· ·— ·—··

— ···· ——— ·— ——· ····

—· ··· ·— —· —·· ··—· · ·

·—·· ·· —· ——· ··· ·—·—·—

·—— ···· ·— — —·· ———

—·— ——— ··— — ···· ··

My journal of thoughts and feelings

What surprises you?

Thoughts: DATE

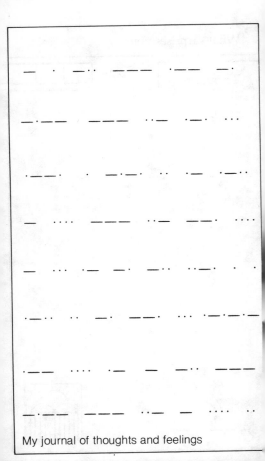

My journal of thoughts and feelings

How could you treat yourself better?

Thoughts:

DATE

.-- ... .- - -.. ---

-.-- --- ..- - ... ..

-. .-. .-. . . .-..

-... . .-- . ... .

.. --. .-. -.. --- -.

--- - .-. . .- ..-.

.-. .- .. .-. -

--- .-- .-. .. ..

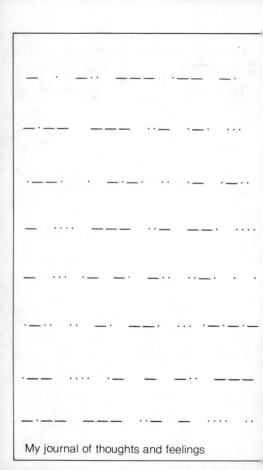

My journal of thoughts and feelings

Thoughts: DATE [ ][ ][ ]

.-- ... .- -- -.. ---

-.-- --- -.. - ... ..

-. -.- ..-. . .-..

-... . .-.. .. . .

.. -.. -.. --- -.

--- - -... . .- ..-.

.-. -.. -

--- .- -.- ..

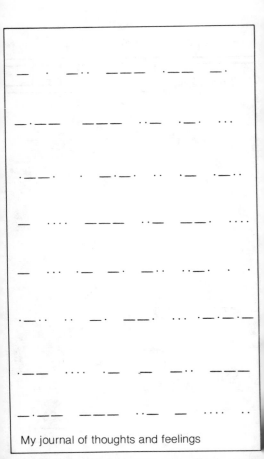

My journal of thoughts and feelings

Thoughts: DATE

```
.__   ...   ._   _   _   _..   ___

_.__   ___   .._   _   ...   ..

_.   ._.   .._.   .   ._..

_...   .   ._   ._   ..   _   ._

.._   _..   ___   _.

___   _   _...   .   ._   .._.

._.   .   ..   _   ._

___   ._   ._   ..
```

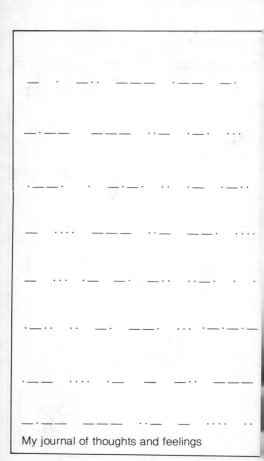

My journal of thoughts and feelings

What are the things that give you peace
of mind and help restore you?

Thoughts: DATE ☐ ☐ ☐

.—— ... .— — —.. ———

—.—— ——— ..— — .... ..

—.— .— — ..— . . .—..

—... . .—— — . ...— .

.. .— —.. ——— —.

——— — ..—.. . .— . ..—

.—. . .. .. — .—..

—— .—— .— .. ..

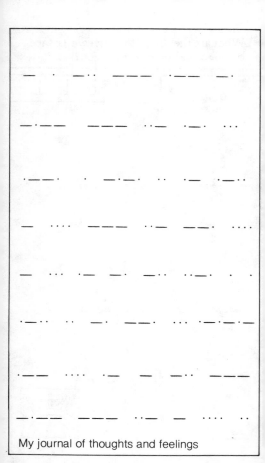

My journal of thoughts and feelings

When you were a child and peered into the future, what did you think life would be like?

Thoughts: DATE [ ][ ][ ]

.——— .... .— — —.. ———

—.—— ——— ... — .... ..

—. —.— ..— . . —..

—... . .—.. .. . ...— .

..—.. —.. _ ——— —.

——— — — —... . .— . ..—.

.—. .— .. —

My journal of thoughts and feelings

Thoughts: DATE

___ ... __ _ _.. ___

_.__ ___ .._ _ ... ..

_. _._ .._. . . ._..

_.. . .__ .. . .._ .

.. .. _.. ___ _ _.

___ _ _ _.. . ._ .._

._ . ._ .. _.. .

___ .__ ._. ..

My journal of thoughts and feelings

What kind of person do you want to be?

Thoughts:

.—— ... .—— — — —.. ———

—.—— ——— .—— — — ... ..

—. —.— .—. . . .—..

—.. . .—.. . . ...—. .

.. ——. —.. ——— —.

———— — —.. . .— ..—.

.—. .— —. —.. ..

———— .—.. .—. ..

My journal of thoughts and feelings

, Write something beautiful to the world. (It can be in your secret language.)

Thoughts: DATE [   ] [   ] [   ]

.— ... .— — — —.. ——

—.— ——— ..— —. ... ..

—. —.— ..— . . .—..

—.. . .—.. .. . ...— .

..——.. —.. ——— —.

——— — —.. . .— ..—.

.—. .—. .. —.. —

——— ·—— ·—· ·· — ·

—·· ——— ·—— —· —·——

——— ··— ·—· ··· ·——·

· —·—· ·· ·— ·—·· — ····

——— ··— ——· ···· — ···

·— —· —·· ··—· · · ·—··

·· —· ——· ··· ·—·—·—

·—— ···· ·— — —·· ———

—·—— ——— ··— — ···· ··

My journal of thoughts and feelings

If you could be a musical instrument
what would you be?

Thoughts:

DATE

.--- ... .-- -- -.. ---

-.-- --- .. -- ... ..

-.-- .-- ..-- . . .-..

-..- . .-.. .. . ...

.. --.. -.. --- -.

--- -- -.. . .- -..

.-. .- .. -.. -

--- .-- .-. -. ..

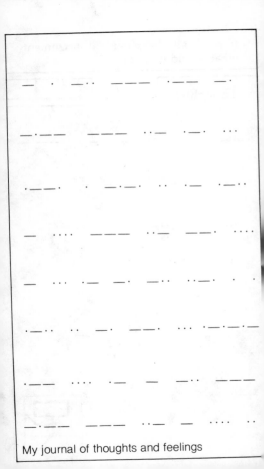

My journal of thoughts and feelings

What is the very worst thing that can happen to you?

Thoughts: DATE | | | |

.___ ... ._ _ _ _.. ___

_.__ ___ .._ _ _ ... ..

_. _._ .._ _ _ .__..

_.. . .__ .. . ..._ .

.._.. _.. ___ _.

___ _ _... . ._ .._.

._. ._ .. _ .. _

___ ._ .__ .. ..

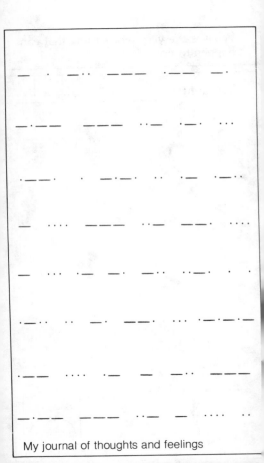

My journal of thoughts and feelings

What do you love?

Thoughts: DATE

.__ ... ._ _ _.. ___

_.___ ___ .._ _ ... ..

_. _._ .._. . . ._..

_... . ._.. .. . ..__ .

.. ._ _.. ___ _.

___ _ _.._ . ._ ._..

._. ._ .. _.. _

___ ._ ._. ..

My journal of thoughts and feelings

What would you do with the freedom
you always wanted? What kind of person would you be?

Thoughts: DATE ☐ ☐ ☐

.__   ...   ._ _ _..   ___

_.__   ___   .._ _   ...   ..

_.   _._   .._. . .   ._..

_... .   ._.. ..   .   .._ .

.. ___..   ._.. _..   ___   _.

___   _   _.. .   ._   .._.

._.   ._   ..   _..   _

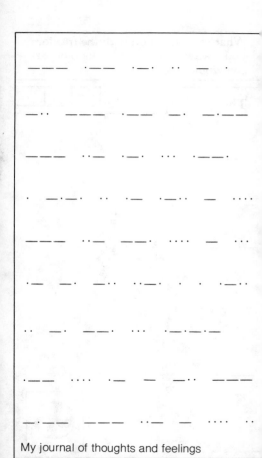

My journal of thoughts and feelings

What are your deepest dreams?

Thoughts: DATE [ ][ ][ ]

.___ ... ._ _ _.. ___

_.__ ___ _ ._ ... ..

_. _._ .._. . . ._..

._.. . ._.. .._.. . .__ .

..__.. _.. ___ _.

___ _ ._ ._ .._.

._. ._ .. ._ .._ _

___ .__ ._ ..

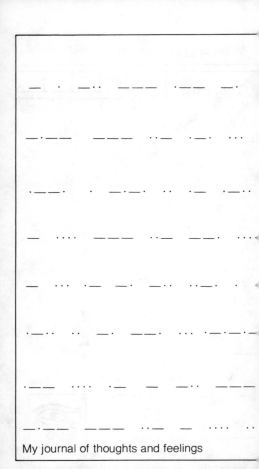

— · —·· ——— ·—— —·

—·—— ——— ··— ·—· ···

·——· · —·—· ·· ·— ·—··

— ···· ——— ··— ——· ···

— ··· ·— —· —·· ·—· ·

·—·· ·· —· ——· ··· ·—·—·

·—— ···· ·— — —·· ———

—·—— ——— ··— — ···· ··

My journal of thoughts and feelings

If you could be an animal, what would
you be?

Thoughts:
DATE

.--- ... .-- - -.. ---

-.--- --- ..- - ... ..

-. -.- ..-. . . .-..

-... . .-.. .. . .

..--.. -.. --- -.

--- - -... . .- ..-

.-. .- .. -..- -

--- .-- .- ..

My journal of thoughts and feelings

If you were to shock yourself out of your set ways, what would you do?

Thoughts: DATE

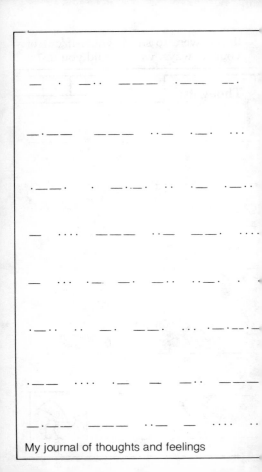

My journal of thoughts and feelings

What are the things that strike you funny?

Thoughts:

DATE

.–– ... .– –– –.. –––

–.–– –––– ..– –– ... ..

–. –.– ..–. .– .–..

–... . .–.. . ... .

..–.. –.– ––– –.

––– – –.. . .– ..–..

.–. .– .. –.. ––

––– .–– .–.. ..

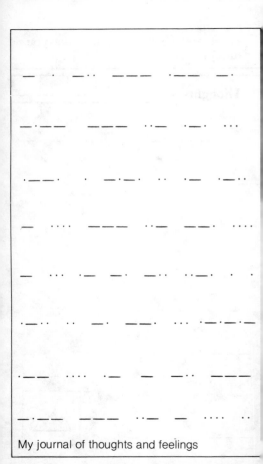

My journal of thoughts and feelings

What are you thankful for?

Thoughts: DATE [　][　][　]

.—— ... .— — —.. ———

—.—— ——— ..— — ... ..

—. —.— ..—. . . .—..

—.. . .—.. . ... .

.. ——.. —.— ——— —.

——— — —.. . .— ..—.

.—. .— .. —.— —

——— .—— .—. ..

My journal of thoughts and feelings

What are the guiding values of your life?

Thoughts:

DATE

.—— ... .— — —.. ———

—.—— ——— .. — ... ..

—. .—.— ..—. . .— ..—..

—... . .—.— . ...— .

.. —.. —.. — —.

——— — —... . .— ..—.

.—. .— .. —.. —

——— .—— .—. ..

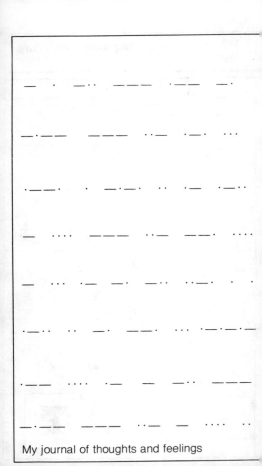

My journal of thoughts and feelings

What is the most wonderful idea you
have had in your life?

Thoughts: DATE [ ][ ][ ]

·—— ··· ·— — — —·· ———

—·—— ——— ··— — ··· ··

—· —·— ··—· · · ·—··

—··· · ·—·· · · ··—· ·

··—·· —·· ——— —·

——— — —··· ·— ·—·

·—· ·· ··—· —

——— ·—· ·—· ··

My journal of thoughts and feelings

If you could be a different element—
earth, water, air or fire—which would
you be?

Thoughts: DATE

.— ...   .—   —   —..   —...

—.——   ———   ...   —   ...   ..

—.   —.—   ..—.   .   .   .—..

—...   .   .—..   ..   .   .

..   —..   .—..   ———   —.

———   —   —..   .   .—   ..—.

.—.   .   .—   ..   —..   —

My journal of thoughts and feelings

What is the prayer you often say to
yourself?

Thoughts:

.— ... .— — —.. —— —

—.—— ——— .. — ... ..

—. —.— ..— . . .—..

—... . .—.. .. . .

.. .—— —.. ——— —— —.

——— —— —... . .— ..—.

.—. .— .. .—.. —

——— .—— .—. ..

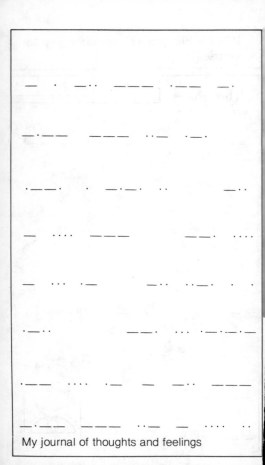

My journal of thoughts and feelings

What things would you do to change
the world?

Thoughts: DATE [   ][   ][   ]

.—— ... .— — —.. ———

—.—— ——— ..— — ... ..

—. —.— ..—. . . .—..

—... . .—.. .. . ...— .

..——.. —.. ——— —.

——— — —... . .— ..—.

.—. .—.. .. —.. ...—.

——— .—— .—. ..

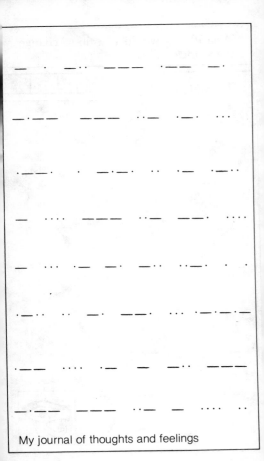

My journal of thoughts and feelings

What are your own questions? (Remember to listen to your voice. Do not be afraid.)

Thoughts: DATE [ ][ ][ ]

.___ ... .__ _ _.. ___

_.__ ___ .._ .._ _ ... ..

_. _._ ..__ . . ._..

_... . ._.. .. . ...__ .

.. .__.. _.. ___ _

.__ _ _... . ._ ._..

.._. ._ .. _.. _

```
--- .-- .--. .. - .

-.. --- .-- -. -.--

--- ..- .- ... .-.

. -.-. .. .- .-.. - ...

--- ..- --. .... - ...

.- -. -.. ..-. . . .--..

.. -. --. ... .-.-.-

.-- .... .- - -.. ---

-.-- --- ..- - .... ..
```

My journal of thoughts and feelings

Thoughts:

·——   ···   ·—   —   —··   ———

·——   ———   ··—   —   —   ···   ··

—·   —·—   ··—·   ·   ·   ·—··

—···   ·   ·—··   ··   ·   ···   ·

··—··   —··   ———   —·

———   —   —···   ·   ·—   ··—·

·—·   ·—   ··   ·—··   —

——— ·—— ·—· ·· — ·

—·· ——— ·—— —· —·——

——— ···— ·—· ··· ·——·

· —·—· ·· ·— ·—·· — ····

——— ···— ——· ···· — ···

·— —· —·· ··—· · · ·——·

·· —· ——· ··· ·—·—·

·—— ···· ·— — —·· ———

—·—— ——— ··— — ···· ··

My journal of thoughts and feelings

WILLIAM ZIMMERMAN, the creator of A BOOK OF QUESTIONS has been a questioner all his life. A journalist for more than 25 years, Mr. Zimmerman is deputy business editor of New York Newday, a daily newspaper. His other books are: HOW TO TAPE INSTANT ORAL BIOGRAPHIES ; MAKE BELIEFS, a gift book for the imagination that readers can complete with pencil, crayon, or paintbrush, and LIFELINES: A Book of Hope, which offers comforting thoughts to help people get through difficult times in life.

GUARIONEX PRESS (pronounced Gwah-ree-oh-nex) was named after a proud Taino Indian chief who lived in Puerto Rico in the sixteenth century. He fought bravely and fiercely against the Spanish, leading the last major Indian insurrection against the war-hardened, better-armed Spanish Army. When Zimmerman and his wife, who is Puerto Rican, decided to start their kitchen-table press in 1979, they knew they too, would have to be brave in order to survive as a small business and named their press Guarionex.

*Gifts for your imagination
from Guarionex Press*

HOW TO TAPE INSTANT ORAL BIOGRAPHIES
by William Zimmerman

Step by step, a journalist shows you and your family how to tape record, videotape or film your life stories, memories and traditions.

112 pages with photos, $8.95 each by mail order (including postage) from Guarionex Press or $6.95 in stores. ISBN 0-935966-00-5, 6"x 9", for all ages.

MAKE BELIEFS: A Gift for Your Imagination
by Bill Zimmerman
drawings by Tom Bloom

This coloring playbook lets you see the world differently—with help from a special question-answer format that encourages you to imagine, and which you complete with crayon, pencil or paintbrush.

96 pages with over 70 drawings, $8.95 each by mail order (including postage) from Guarionex Press or $6.95 in stores. ISBN 0-935966-03-X, 6"x 9", for all ages.